No Hissy Fits!

A Southern Book of Manners

Written by Kelly Kazek

Illustrated by Michelle Hazelwood Hyde

Visit us at **southernthing.com**

Printed in Canada
First edition October 2021
ISBN: 978-1-57571-901-6 (hardback)

"Potluck Day! It's Potluck Day!"

Charley gave a squeal,

And ran into the kitchen

Where Mama packed the meal.

Cheese
Macaroni
Cheddar Cheese
Butter
4. Milk

Charley hugged her brother, Will
Because it was Potluck Day,
When they had nothing more to do
Than eat and drink and play.

Every family brought a dish
Then gathered as a whole,
To line up umpteen tables
Filled with umpteen casseroles.

When Mama said, “It’s time to go,”

And all the goodies were packed,

Dad told Charley and little Will,

“Now, remember how to act.”

"When we are out with others
There are certain things we do,
We must mind our manners
So let's have a quick review."

Ma'am and Sir

When addressing grown-up neighbors

Like Mr. and Mrs. Ham,

Instead of a simple yes or no

You should add a "sir" or "ma'am."

"No, ma'am

No Hissy Fits

We want to act our nicest
Don't get mad and cry or quit,
Potluck Day is not the time
To pitch a hissy fit.

Be Patient

There's plenty of food for everyone

If you push this way and that,

The tables might get tipsy

And the deviled eggs might go SPLAT!

Please and Thank You

Everyone needs help sometimes

It's always fine to ask,

Just be sure to say a "please" up front

And add a "thank you" last.

Listen

When someone else is talking

Listen to their words,

If everyone tries to speak at once

Only the loudest can be heard.

Be a Good Sport

Sometimes it's hard to lose a game
Sometimes it seems unfair,
But if you make a pouty face
Your frown just might stay there.

Share

When gathering with others

Sharing is much more fun,

Unless a bear wants his share

And then you'd better run!

BURP!

Excuse Me

If you give a loud bu-u-u-urrrp

Or spill the bowl of peas,

Be responsible for your acts

And say, "Excuse me, please!"

CHIPS
COOKIES

Clean Up

If everyone made a
really big mess,

And left a ginormous pile of goo,

You might end up with crumbs
in your hair

And banana pudding
in your shoe.

No Hurtful Words

Think of words you'd like to hear

When someone speaks to you,

If you want to be a better friend

Only the nicest words will do.

Charley and Will told Mom and Dad
They would do their very best,
To follow each and every rule
And be considerate guests.

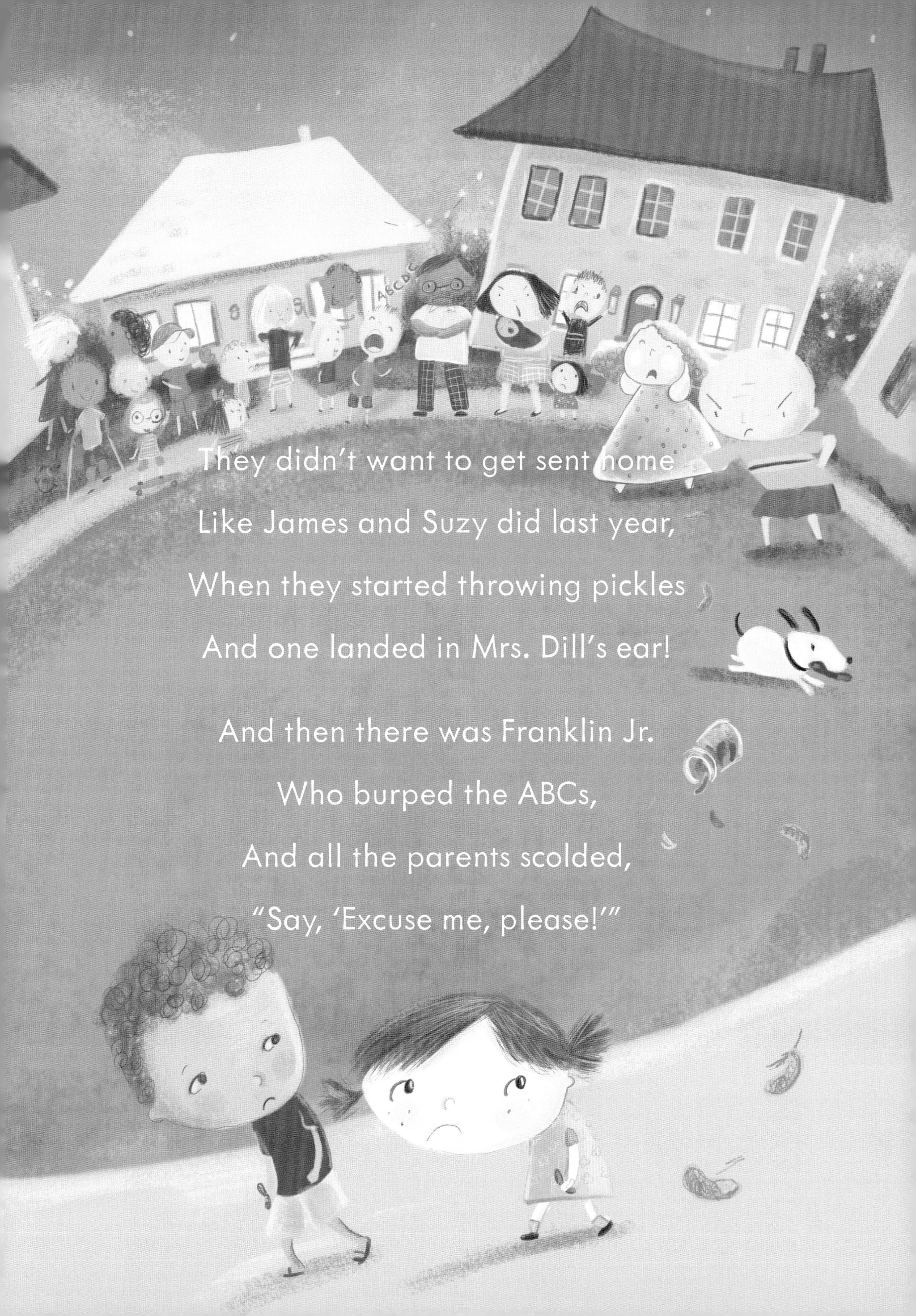

They didn't want to get sent home
Like James and Suzy did last year,
When they started throwing pickles
And one landed in Mrs. Dill's ear!

And then there was Franklin Jr.
Who burped the ABCs,
And all the parents scolded,
"Say, 'Excuse me, please!'"

So Charley minded all the rules
And Will did the best he could,
Mostly, being nice was easy
And having manners felt good.

Their friends shared their toys and games
And only fussed a little bit,
And when they had to wait in line
No one pitched a hissy fit.

Potluck Day was so much fun!

Everyone had a blast,

And Charley remembered
as she left

To add a
"thank you" last.